# FROM THE Land

## maine farms at work

*photographs by* BRIDGET BESAW
*text by* JOHN PIOTTI

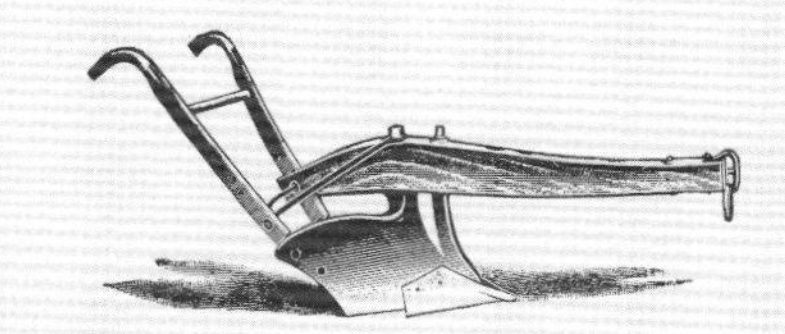

*with a preface by*
CHELLIE PINGREE
US Congress

*The integrity of communities and of human culture ultimately rests on the biological integrity of the landscape in which they are embedded. Our desire to protect this land embodies this idea. This is our effort to begin to restore the balance.*

—Steve Miller
Miller Farm

STEVE WALKS TO MORNING HARVEST

*This book is dedicated to the lifelong farmers who keep our agrarian culture alive by passing on their knowledge of the land; to the young farmers who bring new spirit and healthy food to our tables; and to the next generation of farmers who don't yet realize their talent for working the land—or the role they will play in our community.*

*May the land be there for them to follow their hearts.*

# Contents

*People enjoy the vista. The ocean, the mountaintop, and the field are vistas that like the others pull our attention outward from ourselves.*

—George Christopher
Christopher Farm

MORNING FOG, GEORGE'S HAY FIELD

# Preface

## Chellie Pingree

LIKE MANY YOUNG PEOPLE IN THE 1970s, I found my way to a Maine island with a copy of Helen and Scott Nearing's *Living the Good Life* under my arm and, frankly, a lot to learn about farming. That said, farming wasn't new to me. My grandparents were Scandinavian immigrants, who created a dairy farm in the rich black soil of southern Minnesota. After I migrated to Maine, I had the good fortune to study organic farming at College of the Atlantic with Eliot Coleman and to be a part of the beginnings of the Maine Organic Farmers and Gardeners Association (MOFGA) when people like Paul and Molly Birdsall were pioneers of the "back to the land" movement.

By the time I was raising the first of my three children, I had rented a farm of my own, complete with milking cows, chickens, pigs, and two acres of vegetables that found a ready market with summer visitors. It wasn't hard to find an answer to my many questions—from the county extension agent to the MOFGA newsletter to the wonderful friends and neighbors I was able to tap for information and assistance. I also found that so many of my fellow island residents were exactly the mentors I needed—whether they had a small garden, still kept animals, or just had wonderful memories of the days when our island of North Haven, like so many coastal communities, was sending fresh produce to cities as far as Boston and beyond.

In spite of the activity of the early 1970s, farms were steadily disappearing and when I arrived in the Maine State Senate in 1992, with a seat on the agriculture committee, I witnessed a very stark economic picture for Maine's proud farming families. From dairy farmers to apple growers, our committee heard testimony from one family after another who weren't sure how much longer they could hold on to the land and buildings often in their family's possession for generations.

This book brings us the stories of the reversal. The photos of young faces out seeding the lettuce and bringing the results to the local farmers markets that are growing in communities across the state remind us of the many young farmers who are finding their way to the land—often with an older land owner happy to mentor them in their craft. Our growing farmers markets, the restaurants that proudly advertise local foods, and the "CSAs" (community supported agriculture) that find themselves oversubscribed quickly give us the evidence that

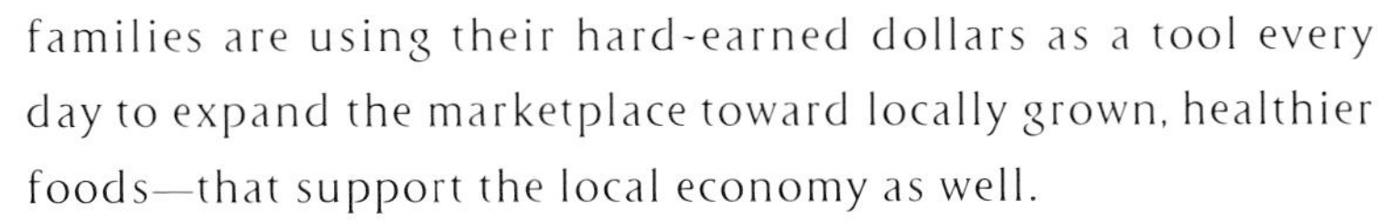

families are using their hard-earned dollars as a tool every day to expand the marketplace toward locally grown, healthier foods—that support the local economy as well.

Today, my partner and I are reviving a 200-year-old farm in our island community. We're even incorporating a few updated techniques like growing our greens in moveable greenhouses and using more modern techniques in our dairy. We are producing organic vegetables, meats, and cheeses for our restaurant and the farmers market. When my constituents call to express their concerns about the toxins in our diet, the relationship of processed school lunches to childhood obesity, or just the challenges that local slaughterhouses face, I can nod with the knowledge of one who is experiencing the same concerns and working in all ways toward a solution. It is a good feeling.

Much like this book is, which brings us beauty and hope. This book profiles just a few of the wonderful farms—both new and old—that are quintessential Maine. This book also shows us the good and important work that Maine Farmland Trust is doing to keep us on a path of expansion, possibilities, and hope.

*In this area there's a real quality of life aspect to having not just farmland, but active farms. Certainly people like being able to purchase food directly from us, but we also provide a sense of place that defines the community.*

—Nate Drummond
Six River Farm

CRANE BROTHERS HARVESTING POTATOES AT DAWN

*Seventy-five years ago, there were 500 farms in this area. Ten years ago, there were only 2 or 3. But now that is changing. There has been a vigorous rebirth as the numbers of young farmers have grown in the past few years. They've doubled the membership of the grange, and now you see the oldest and the youngest generation of farmers under one roof. It's beginning to feel like a return to what used to be here.*

— George Christopher
Christopher Farm

---

KALE HARVEST AT FISH BOWL FARM

# Farming, Farmers, & Farmland

JOHN PIOTTI

IN MAINE AND ELSEWHERE, farming and farmers are all too frequently viewed as relics of the past. They are often portrayed sentimentally, nostalgically. Or we see them simplified—at times even demeaned—in the style of "country cute."

The truth is that farming remains a vital part of Maine's economy, landscape, and social fabric. And Maine's farmers are not country bumpkins, but some of the ablest people I know.

Farming in Maine is a $2 billion industry. It is the economic foundation of much of rural Maine and the soul of many communities. Doubt it? Ask around about who shops at the local hardware store rather than the Big Box twenty miles away, or who many towns rely on to serve on the board of selectmen or budget committee or fire department, or who the Grange finds to cook and serve Saturday's public supper—as often as not, it's farmers and their families.

Maine's farmers are an impressive lot. The standouts are simultaneously adept at growing crops, fixing machinery, caring for livestock, conceiving new products, and selling what they've created with a depth of knowledge and conviction that only comes from having sweat every detail and labored over every task. I've worked closely with farmers for fifteen years, so I've witnessed this firsthand. (And I've been repeatedly humbled by the tomatoes and corn and pumpkins that these talented folk produce, the likes of which my wife Susan and I can never raise in our garden. I'm in awe on multiple levels.)

Farming in Maine defies any single label. It is at once robust, thriving, threatened, modern, ancient, venerable, dirty, tedious, and hip. It is as diverse and complex as the thousands of Maine farmers whose labor and love steward a million acres of working landscape.

Farming here is growing and poised to grow more. Maine has abundant water, good soils, handy access to markets, intact farm infrastructure, and a nice balance between established farmers and young people entering the field. Consumers, meanwhile, increasingly care about where their food comes from—they are demanding exactly what Maine farmers can provide.

Bridget Besaw and I envisioned a book that captures the vibrancy of Maine's farms, calling attention to what's happening here and sharing our excitement about farming's future.

We want to convey some of what farmers are doing with new crops and new growing methods and new ways to reach customers. Maine now produces a wider array of vegetables and grains and livestock than ever before. Many farmers now lengthen their season using cold frames and hoop houses, while others employ heated greenhouses to grow year-round. Beef cattle are increasingly raised on grass—something Maine grows very well; and farmers are using ingenious pasturing systems that integrate different kinds of livestock to good effect. On top of it all, more farmers are selling direct to customers through farmers markets or farm stands or so-called "CSAs" (community supported agriculture), where patrons buy a "share" in a farm's harvest and then periodically receive baskets of produce.

There's no question that some farms are struggling. Dairy farms—for instance—are clearly in crisis. But the primary problem within the dairy sector is a faulty federal pricing system, not

Maine's inability to make milk economically. Over time, either federal policy will change or Maine's farmers will—just as our farmers have done for the past 400 years. (The story of farming in Maine is a story of constant change.)

But in this age, the fear is that a farm will transition from a working landscape to a subdivision, rather than from one type of farm to another. This isn't due to a lack of viable farming opportunities, because we know such opportunities are out there and growing. Instead, the problem is that society as a whole has not yet realized that farms can provide an ongoing economic return that dwarfs the one-time payoff that comes from new development. Too many people simply don't believe farming has a future.

Fortunately, this perception is changing. More and more people—though not yet nearly enough—are catching on that we cannot live sustainably without local farms. Farming is not anything but nostalgic, it's a necessity.

In both words and photographs, Bridget and I want to communicate some of the ways farming is changing. Simply put, farming in Maine is very different than it was a generation ago. A given farm may not have changed much, but farming has—often in ways that aren't readily seen or commonly understood.

Here are some of those changes:

- The number of farms in Maine is growing. From 2002 to 2007, Maine went from 7,199 farms to 8,136 farms—a remarkable 13 percent increase in only five years. Most of the new farms are small operations serving local markets. (Source: USDA's Agricultural Census, published every five years.)
- Many Maine farms, not just newly established farms, are now selling locally. Indeed, almost all of Maine's older orchards that remain in business have survived by changing their focus to local markets.
- Farms are growing a much broader assortment of products. Maine agriculture has always been more than potatoes, milk, and blueberries; but as more farms grow other products and sell them locally, the full bounty of what's produced here comes into view—from winter greens to

naturally raised meats to farmstead cheeses. As a result, local consumers have begun to think differently about what Maine can grow, and this in turn creates even more opportunities for innovative farmers.

- Some farms that because of their small size wouldn't have been considered true farms a generation ago are thriving under new strategies that change how we think about farming. As one example, an increasing number of small farms are growing high-value crops that require a lot of care and attention but not much space, such as organic herbs and certain vegetables. A farmer with the right skills and market savvy might earn as much pursuing this strategy on 5 acres as a farmer working 500 acres of commodity crops.
- Some farms have remained viable by becoming larger. The number of farms over a thousand acres has quadrupled in twenty years. (Note: Even Maine's largest farms are small compared with what's common in many other states.) The growth of large farms seems at odds with the fact that some of the greatest new opportunities reside in smaller operations focused on local markets. But what's happening is that different types of opportunities are emerging for different sized farms. Larger farms serving commodity markets often grow to capture economies of scale, while smaller farms often diversify and market directly. At present, both strategies work.
- Larger farms and smaller farms are interconnected and mutually supportive. Larger farms produce the vast bulk of agricultural goods and are the reason Maine retains milk processors, grain infrastructure, farm equipment dealers, and the like. So if Maine's larger farms disappeared, smaller farms would likely pay more for grain and possibly have no place to ship milk. They would also have a harder time finding a mechanic who can fix a tractor or a banker who will write them a loan. Conversely, larger farms benefit from the renewed public support for agriculture that comes from smaller farms forging such direct links to local consumers. In addition, some larger farms who see the power of local marketing are experimenting with doing the same with a portion of their own crops. For instance,

more than one large potato farm in Aroostook County is now growing a few acres of organic potatoes for sale to restaurants and specialty stores, in addition to a primary crop of conventional potatoes sold as commodities.

A different kind of change—no less significant—is how Maine's farming community now views farmland preservation. A generation ago, few farmers knew about preserving land through agricultural easements, and most of the farmers who were aware of this tool dismissed it as unnecessary or even misguided. Indeed, up to about a decade ago—when Maine Farmland Trust was formed—the focus of both farmers and folks like me who worked with farmers was on keeping farms profitable. Our shared belief was that profitable farms would remain in business, and

that if we focused on helping farms prosper, the land would stay working without the need for easements.

There is a certain logic to this approach—to a point. And that point is when the farm changes hands. Then, the very same farm could be growing the same crops and supplying the same markets, but if the new owner incurred an extra high level of debt to purchase the property, the economic equation could be vastly different. A once profitable farm could become unprofitable overnight, simply because the farmer needed to pay as much for that land as someone who intended to subdivide it into house lots.

What an increasing number of Maine farmers now realize is that preserving farmland is critical to keeping farming viable. Perhaps the biggest threat to farming's future is that farmers

cannot afford to pay a developer's price for land they intend to work. However, once preserved through an easement, farmland forever sells at its value as farmland, not as future development. Preserving more farmland will allow more new farmers to get started, and help existing farmers expand operations or secure land they currently lease. Beyond this, many existing farmers see good reason to sell or donate an easement because of the resulting financial benefits (cash or tax savings).

For these reasons, and none too soon, farmland preservation has finally come into its own in Maine. As much as one-third of Maine's most productive farmland (up to 400,000 acres) will likely change hands in the next 10 to 15 years, as an aging population of landowners sell or die. This demographic challenge is coming just as farming in Maine is poised for a renaissance—just as many farmers have embraced exciting new business strategies and many consumers have avidly begun to demand more local foods.

There is great opportunity here—to preserve much of this farmland that will be changing hands, and to continue to put it in the hands of committed farmers.

The stories of seven farms contained in this book show how Maine Farmland Trust works to preserve farmland and enhance farming. Different strategies work for different farms. Some landowners are in a position to donate an easement, while others seek to sell their development rights to raise funds to reinvest in the farm. Still other farmers have no option except to sell the land outright; and Maine Farmland Trust will now buy a farm, preserve it, then resell it to another farmer at an affordable "farmland" value.

Another strategy is FarmLink, a service through which Maine Farmland Trust matches people looking for farms with landowners wishing to sell or lease. Though this doesn't result in permanent protection, it gets a new farmer on the land during this critical period for Maine agriculture. In a few short years, FarmLink has made over fifty "links"—that's fifty farms that will likely keep working for at least another generation.

I'm proud of the work Maine Farmland Trust has done, often in partnership with local or regional land trusts. But we could not do a thing without the farmers who work with us. They are the ones who know the land and have committed their lives to it.

Maine farmers shepherd small miracles every day. They tend the soil and plants and animals that—literally—sustain us. They make it possible for us to obtain good food close to home. They enrich our rural communities, and steward our most cherished landscapes.

A generation from now, I'm convinced that organizations like Maine Farmland Trust won't need to be preserving farmland, not because all the good farmland will already be preserved, but because society will recognize that the highest and best use of farmland will be to grow food and fiber. But until that day comes, I find solace in countless Maine farmers who dismiss short-term returns and shortsighted economics, and who focus instead with clear vision on a better future.

# An Introduction to Seven Maine Farms

FOR THE PURPOSES OF THIS BOOK, we chose seven farms that capture some of what's happening in Maine while showcasing different ways to approach farmland preservation. Though working farms exist across the state in over 500 communities, we chose seven that are located in just five towns. We did so because it lets us tell a few stories about how neighboring farmers support each other, and how a successful farm seldom operates in isolation.

For eight generations, the same family has farmed **McDougal Orchards** in Springvale. They have kept the farm viable through innovation, by changing what they grow, and how they market. The diversified farm now raises a variety of fruits and vegetables. Some of it is sold to local supermarkets and some is marketed on site to customers who come to the farm, in part for the experience. The farm is permanently preserved through an easement held by Maine Farmland Trust, for which the McDougals were compensated by the State of Maine through the Land for Maine's Future program.

**Fish Bowl Farm** and **Six River Farm** are located adjacent to each other in Bowdoinham, and are operated by young farmers who have been very successful growing premium vegetables that they sell at farmers markets and to discerning restaurants. They lease land from George Christopher, a visionary farmer who has

transformed his own holdings into a "farm incubator," which now provides land, housing, and other support to half a dozen start-up operations. George has bequeathed his property to Maine Farmland Trust, so that it may continue to serve young farmers long into the future.

Located in Exeter, **Crane Brothers Farm** is the largest potato farm in central Maine. It's a true family affair, and considerable family effort has gone into planning for the future—at the same time that considerable resources have gone into securing additional land. Though the farm's holdings have not yet been permanently preserved through easements, there is now a clear plan and commitment to continue farming through the next generation. Family patriarch Neil Crane serves on Maine Farmland Trust's board.

**Horsepower Farm** in Penobscot grows a broad array of organic vegetables, and does so—as its name implies—using horses for plowing and cultivating. Operated by Paul Birdsall, now with his son and grandson, the farm also relies heavily on apprentices. Over the years, Paul has been a mentor to dozens of young farmers. He has also been a pioneer in farmland preservation. Paul not only donated an easement on his own farm, but has been a force behind the preservation of many other farms in the area. Paul is one of the founders of Maine Farmland Trust.

Also in Penobscot is **Quills End Farm**, where Paul Birdsall and Maine Farmland Trust helped attract new farmers. The Retbergs raise livestock (cows, goats, pigs, and chickens) and maintain a large garden and a sizable woodlot. Like many farmers, Philip Retberg also works off the farm, at least for now, and Heather home schools their three children. Located in a part of Maine that is increasingly popular (and pricey), this property was only affordable because—as preserved land—it sold at "farmland" value, not development value.

The **Miller Farm** in Westmanland has no farm sign or logo or website. Steve and Barbara Miller think of themselves as homesteaders more than farmers. But for years they have supported themselves almost exclusively from the income they make selling farm products, mostly honey, berries, and nursery stock. They also steward an ecologically rich forest. They donated an easement to Maine Farmland Trust because they care deeply about what they have created over the last 35 years and wish to see it endure.

*Robert McDougal, McDougal Orchards; Nate Drummond & Gabrielle Gosselin, Six River Farm; Neil Crane, Crane Brothers Farm; Paul Birdsall, Horsepower Farm; Heather & Carolyn Retberg, Quills End Farm; Barbara & Steve Miller, Miller Farm.*

# McDougal Orchards

*Starting from about 1790, there's Joshua one, Joshua two, Ben, George, my father, and me. Now the next generation is Ellen—that makes seven, and then of course with Matthew and Polly and Ryan, you're up to about eight generations. You just keep your fingers crossed for the future.*

— Robert McDougal
McDougal Orchards

THINK "MAINE FARM" and you may well conjure up an image remarkably similar to McDougal Orchards on a summer day. The clean white farmhouse connected to a large white barn. Row upon long row of apple trees and corn. Ridge-top views to the western mountains. And everywhere, a thousand shades of green, speckled here and there with yellow and gold and (as summer lingers and those apples ripen) more and more red.

This is a classic Maine farm, in both appearance and history. Like many Maine farms, it has been worked by a single family over many generations. And like many Maine farms, each generation has made changes to keep the farm vital. Two hundred years ago, the McDougal ancestors grew much of what they needed to sustain themselves. Sometime thereafter, they ventured into specialized markets—first sheep and then dairy cows—which

*Robert harvests a few beauties (page 28); on the McDougal farmstead a swing hangs peacefully on the Black Walnut tree planted 110 years ago (page 29); early morning ride to harvest; a family enjoys an autumn hayride through the orchards; portrait of Evan from the farm truck (clockwise, page 30); McDougal garden (above).*

brought in cash, allowing them to limit how many different products they had to grow themselves. After World War I, apples became the crop of choice.

Jump to today. Below this farm's iconic image lies a smart business strategy, tailored to the times. When Maine's ability to compete in world apple markets disappeared a generation ago, many orchards went out of business, while others—including McDougal's—sought new strategies.

"We've gone from feeding the world to feeding our neighbors," explains Ellen McAdam, who farms with various family members, including nephews Ryan and Aaron McDougal—the eighth generation.

Seventy acres of fruit trees have been reduced to seventeen, and the crop is sold locally, at two supermarkets and directly from the farm. The McDougals now grow other kinds of fruit (peaches, nectarines, plums, and raspberries), as well as sweet corn, tomatoes, and pumpkins. And a cousin makes maple syrup. The farm offers a diverse array of products that local people love, in part because they know those delicious fruits and vegetables came to life on that beautiful ridge, nurtured by their talented neighbors.

In the fall, McDougal Orchards comes alive. It's a local tradition to come out to pick apples, taste the season's first cider, and maybe stretch out on the sun-warmed grass or take a hay ride. There are big pumpkins for carving, and a corn maze to get lost in. Ellen's brother Gene brings over his animals at this time to add to the festive feel. There are cattle, sheep, pigs, ducks, and chickens to see and feed.

Some call it "agro-tourism," but really, it's about engaging the community, connecting people to good food and the good folk who raise it. This kind of connection helps sell farm products, but it also builds community support for farming and for preserving farmland.

The McDougal family decided to preserve their farmland because they saw how other local farms had been divided into house lots.

"We didn't want to see our farm go that way," says Robert McDougal, Ellen's father. "But it was our kids who talked us into it. They did the research and convinced us."

The McDougal's vision was to preserve not just their orchards, but also broader family holdings, a full 300 acres known

collectively as the Hanson Farm. After much discussion, the family decided to seek funding under the Land for Maine's Future (LMF) program. LMF would compensate them for the value they'd lose by placing a permanent agricultural easement on their land. Though this funding wasn't the McDougal's motivation for preserving their land, it would come in handy as the family continued to improve their farm operation.

Still, this project would not have happened without strong local support, as is required of all LMF projects. In this case, the community owned an adjacent farm, then being leased, which was a holdover from the days of "town farms" for the poor. The community agreed to place a permanent easement on that 55-acre property, thus contributing local "match" to the project.

The decision to preserve farmland can be complicated and challenging. Certainly the McDougals were faced with the complexities of dealing with so many family members and with maneuvering through the LMF process. (As good as the LMF program is, it is still a government program with hoops to jump through.)

But family members tell me that the decision itself really wasn't so difficult. They believe in the future of farming. Indeed, they are taking steps with their own operation to help ensure that it will continue to be farmed for at least another generation. And they understand how farming in the future is at risk—how even farming on land they own could be at risk—if the underlying resource, the land itself, is not preserved.

"We did what we knew was right," says Robert McDougal. "It was that simple."

*Matthew samples a fresh ear after picking; closing the gate behind the corn trailer; Evan harvesting corn; Robert and grandson Matthew walk home through the orchards (left to right).*

# Fish Bowl Farm *and* Six River Farm

*I get to see food grown and I get to see farmers grow, and that's kind of neat to see two crops at the same time. What's happening here is more than just the crops that are coming out of the ground. These young farmers are making a difference both by growing people's food and by growing an agricultural community.*

—George Christopher
Christopher Farm

DON'T TELL GEORGE CHRISTOPHER that people can't make a living farming. He's been doing so for over 40 years, and now he's helping others get started, hoping that they will be able to make farming their life's work as well.

George is a craggy old farmer—there's no getting around that. But above all, George is an entrepreneur. He's a smart man who sees opportunity all around him. Show him a piece of good cropland within 30 miles of Portland or midcoast markets, as I did once a few years ago, and soon his mind is calculating how much income this property can generate growing vegetables.

"At least $10,000 an acre," he declared as that property's farm potential.

He should know. George has created what he calls a "farm incubator" on 1,000 acres in Bowdoinham, some of which is rich river-bottom land. He leases parcels to young farmers and keeps a distant but watchful eye on their progress. At present, his property boasts seven separate farm operations, which collectively employ over 50 people at the height of the season. There's a dairy farm and land for hay, but George's best soils are for growing vegetables.

Thanks to George, Chris Cavendish now has land to grow a large variety of organic vegetables. Chris started farming here in 2005. He kept the name Fish Bowl Farm that he had adopted when he was the resident farmer at the Common Ground Fair, an annual celebration of rural life run by the Maine Organic Farmers and Gardeners Association (MOFGA), where Chris's operation was on view by 60,000 visitors a year.

When Chris was ready to move on, the opportunity that George provided—to lease good land at a fair price—was exactly what he needed. Like many young farmers who partake in MOFGA's workshops and apprenticeships, Chris had learned how to farm, but he lacked the kind of operational track record that banks look for in making loans. George offered a way for Chris to realize his dream without having to buy the land.

*Gabrielle weeding on an early summer day (page 34); barefooted carrot harvest at Fishbowl Farm (above); Chris takes a rest between rows of Bright Lights swiss chard (pages 36 & 37).*

*I always associate Thanksgiving with the new seed catalogs. When I open them up, I'm like a kid in a candy store. It's hard to stop myself from trying whatever looks new and exciting, or heirloom old and exciting. I think my market customers appreciate that I try new varieties and experiment with vegetables that are harder to find. It's fun for me too.*

—Chris Cavendish
Fish Bowl Farm

CHRIS RESTS IN THE BRIGHT LIGHTS SWISS CHARD

*Sometimes you pinch yourself when you realize that you get to be outside in all kinds of weather during all the seasons and you get to see the full extent of the day from sunrise to sunset—it's an incredible feeling being very much in touch with the elements and their effects on your work.*

—Nate Drummond
Six River Farm

BAREFOOT CARROT HARVEST ON FISH BOWL FARM

Fish Bowl Farm has grown steadily over the past five seasons. Chris now has about ten acres in active cultivation (and almost as much in cover crops, preparing for the next rotation). For those unfamiliar with mixed vegetable operations, ten acres may not sound like much, but it is considerable. We're not talking about acres of a single crop like sweet corn, but smaller patches of 30 to 40 different vegetables. Think about a home garden of, say, 40 feet square, and then multiply that by over 250! During the season each acre demands the skills of many workers.

Nearby, Six River Farm is also part of George's visionary project. Nate Drummond and Gabrielle Gosselin, a couple in their twenties, came to George via FarmLink, a service through which Maine Farmland Trust connects people seeking farms with landowners wishing to sell or lease land. Now in their third season, Nate and Gabrielle are growing six acres of organic vegetables. Like Chris, they had solid experience, having apprenticed on other farms, but wouldn't have been able to afford to buy the kind of land that George offered.

The lure of George's incubator is more than affordability. Nate speaks about not only leasing great land but also having a place to live and access to a walk-in cooler and wash-down facilities.

"It allowed us to focus on our business operation from day one," says Nate. "And to benefit from working with other members of a growing farm community."

Indeed, farms here cooperate actively, sharing equipment, know-how, and simple yet useful information, such as when the season's first potato beetle is seen. But in marketing, these farms are often competitors. For instance, both Fish Bowl Farm and Six River Farm sell directly through the same two farmers markets in Brunswick, and to some of the same restaurants.

Chris, Nate, and Gabrielle represent a new breed of farmer, skilled at both growing and selling. A key to their success is that they market "direct" to patrons at farmers markets, chefs at restaurants, or managers at small stores. These marketing strategies only work, however, because they grow beautiful and absolutely delicious produce that customers increasingly appreciate.

"It comes down to the quality of what we grow," says Nate.

Thanks to the energy and skills of the farmers he leases to,

*There are days when I realize that what I'm planting or weeding or harvesting is going to end up on someone's plate. It comes with a strong feeling of responsibility. It stresses the importance of making sure we are producing healthy nutritional food and we are truly providing something that will help make someone healthier.*

—Nate Drummond
Six River Farm

NATE ON THE TRACTOR THROUGH THE PEAS

George's visionary "farm incubator" is working. Though, like all experiments, it's unclear exactly where this one will lead. It could be that farmers like Chris, Nate, and Gabrielle move on to purchase their own land, enabling a new crop of young farmers to work this land. Or it could be that the farmers now leasing stay indefinitely, and that the "incubation" that occurs leads to creating other new farms in and around Bowdoinham. Indeed, we are seeing the early signs of that kind of farm renaissance in the region, spurred in part by the successful activity on George's land.

One thing is for sure: George's land will remain farmland. He has bequeathed his holdings to Maine Farmland Trust, which will protect this legacy, ensuring that this land can forever be used as it should—to grow nurturing food.

*Carrying a box of freshly harvested carrots at Fishbowl Farm (page 38); Chris tills his soil with a wheel hoe; Nate and Gabrielle plant starters (above, left to right, page 39); Nate on tractor through the peas (pages 40 & 41); hand planting seedlings at Six River Farm (page 42); topping the carrots and sorting by size at Fish Bowl Farm (page 43).*

*Farming is a disruption of nature. I can't replace nature's processes. I will never be able to leave the land significantly better than before it was farmed, but I aim to use what I know of nature's processes to inform the way I farm. It's important that I leave the land in a better condition than when I received it. So I put a lot of organic matter back in the soil, I till it as little as I have to, and one of every three years I let a different parcel of land sit through a full season with cover crop.*

—Chris Cavendish
Fish Bowl Farm

---

CHRIS CARRYING STRAW FOR THE GARLIC FIELD

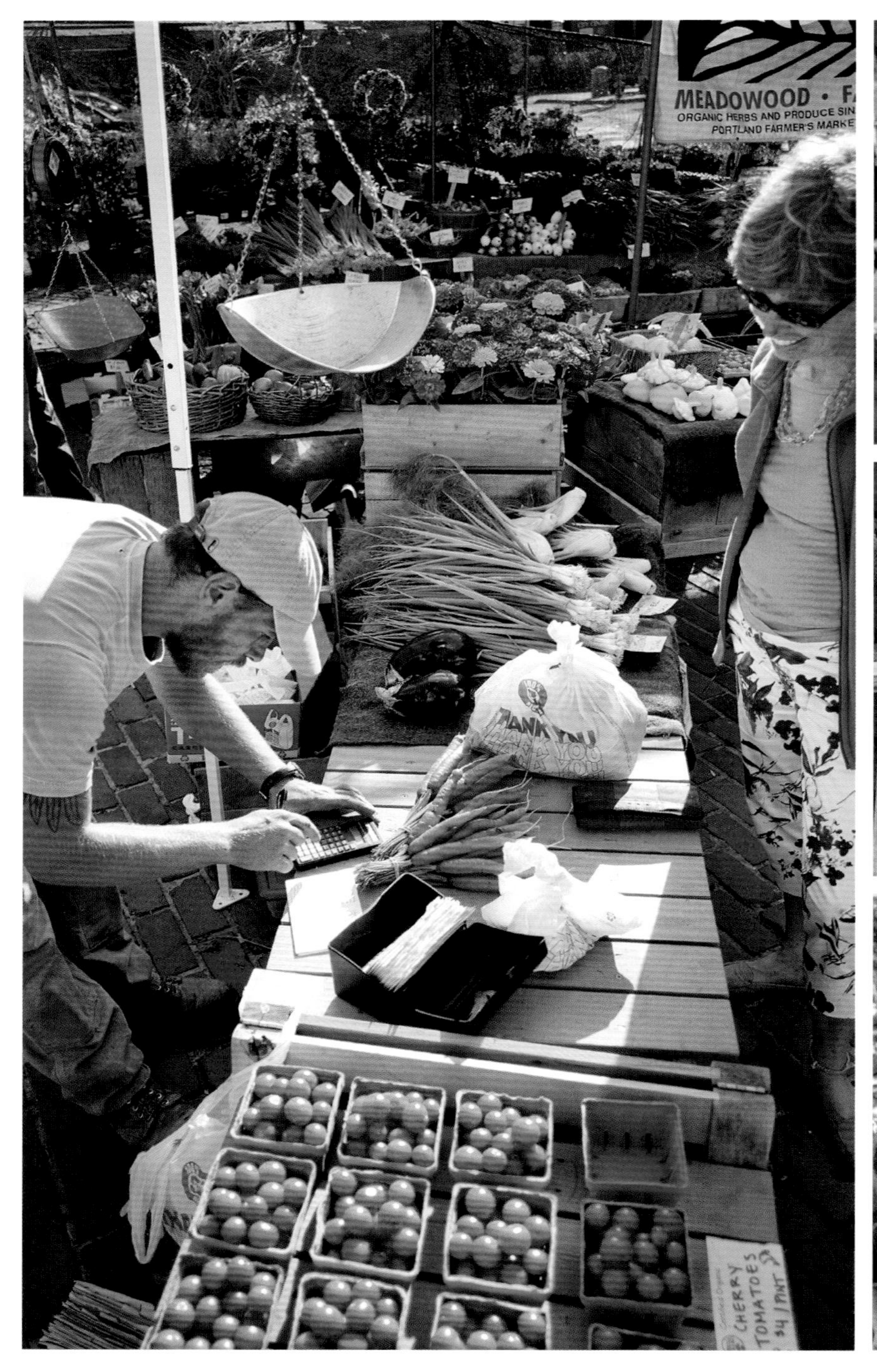
MEADOWOOD
PORTLAND FARMER'S MARKET
CHERRY TOMATOES

ORGANIC
HEIRLOOM
TOMATOES
$3.00/lb

*Chris carries straw to spread among his rows (pages 44 & 45); Chris calculating totals, weighing his famous heirloom tomatoes, and sharing good humor with market customers (page 46); after Saturday farmers market, Chris sells his organic produce and flowers to Portland restaurateurs from the back of his truck (above); Gabrielle harvests zinnias to complement Six River Farm's organic vegetable offerings at the Brunswick farmers market (pages 48 & 49).*

*There's nothing esoteric out here. We can actually physically touch everything that we're doing for our livelihood and our lifestyle. We touch it at every phase, we watch it grow, and we taste it. We get to explore our work with all of our senses. Putting your hands in the dirt and growing food is just about as tangible as it gets.*

— Gabrielle Gosselin
Six River Farm

GABRIELLE HARVESTING ZINNIAS

# Crane Brothers Farm

*A lot of policy that's made in Washington or at the state level is made sometimes without knowledge of what the actual facts are out in the field.*

— Neil Crane
Crane Brothers Farm

NOT ALL OF MAINE'S VEGETABLE OPERATIONS are small, and not all the business opportunities lie with small farms selling locally.

Based in Exeter, Crane Brothers Farm is the largest potato farm in central Maine. Through hard work and good planning, the Cranes continue to support their large, multi-generational family, while keeping almost 4,000 acres of farmland in use. In a given year, they will harvest over 20,000 tons of potatoes, most of which are processed into chips for Frito-Lay. They also grow 1,000 acres of corn, which is sold to Blue Seal for dairy and poultry feed.

Farms in and around Exeter are typically larger than farms further south, and they are not within easy striking distance of growing in-state markets found around Portland or in coastal communities. Consequently, their business models are necessarily different. They generally sell to processors.

In Maine, farms of this size and scale contribute greatly to the health of farming and the protection of farmland. They maintain the critical mass of agricultural activity that sustains key infrastructure, such as grain suppliers and equipment dealers that farms of all sizes rely on. And without such farms, hundreds of thousands of acres of good farmland would likely be converted to house lots.

It is increasingly commonplace in some circles to view larger farms as one of the problems with modern agriculture. But what many people don't realize is that even Maine's largest farms are small by national standards. And like Crane Brothers Farm, they remain true family farms.

Neil Crane is past what would be retirement age in most other professions, and much of what he once did at the farm now falls to the next generation. But his role is still integral to the overall operation. He is commonly at the wheel of some truck or tractor during harvest time. More importantly, he continues to lend his wisdom to the tough decisions inherent in running a complex family business that is wedded to the vagaries of weather and markets.

Neil has a strategic mind. Years before most Maine farmers saw any value in farmland preservation, Neil was pushing the State Legislature to guarantee that a portion of funds from the Land for Maine's Future program (LMF) would purchase

agricultural easements. And at his own farm, he insisted that his family go through a thorough planning process to ensure a clear business strategy was in place to serve the next generation. As part of that strategy, the family has stretched financially to purchase vulnerable farmland.

"It's a different way to preserve farmland," says Neil. "But no less important."

In Maine, many dairy and potato farmers own sizable acreage themselves, but also rely on land owned by others for additional cropland. These lands are often necessary to the farm's economic success, yet not within the farmer's long-term control. Occasionally, there is a formal lease, but more often than not, it's simply a handshake. These parcels are frequently owned by elderly persons who perhaps once farmed the land themselves, and when the owners die or move to a nursing home or relocate to Florida, the property is generally put up for sale at prices many farmers cannot afford.

Whenever possible, the Cranes try to buy any such land that is critical to their operation. However, even this large and successful farm will not always be able to outbid developers. And for many farmers, paying a developer's price for farmland is a pipe dream.

But a solution does exist. Selectively, Maine Farmland Trust has begun to target farmland that is used by farmers who don't own it. We buy and then preserve the land through an agricultural easement, before selling it to that farmer at its "farmland" value (as opposed to its "development" value). "Buy/Protect/Sell"—as we call it—is beginning to make a difference keeping existing farms in business. Not surprisingly, Neil Crane has been a source of encouragement.

Because the Cranes have acted themselves, Maine Farmland Trust has not yet needed to employ a "Buy/Protect/Sell" to secure a key property for them (though we are now exploring one such opportunity). Nor have the Cranes yet placed an easement on land they already own (though that, too, is a future possibility). At present, the Cranes are protecting farmland in other ways—by their commitment to keep farming and buy more farmland when they can.

Different strategies work at different times, for different farms and in different regions.

This region of central Maine is clearly farm country. A traveler here will likely encounter a slow-moving tractor or manure truck on the road. The balance between field and forest feels different than in southern Maine. The land here is more open, a sign of good soils and still prosperous farms. Development pressure is not yet as intense as elsewhere, but it is here and it does hurt. I've witnessed more than one local farmer shake his head at the new house plopped into a once-farmed field.

The Cranes and their neighbors make a living off this land. More than anyone, they understand how preserving the land base is critical to local farming's continued success. Much of Maine Farmland Trust's future work lies within towns like Exeter and with farmers like the Cranes.

*A potato harvester passes by a row of freshly surfaced potatoes (page 50); the Crane Brothers original farmstead; Neil at the wheel of a harvester (left to right, page 51); rock and debris picking from the harvester belt (page 52); a potato harvester makes its way through the rows just before dawn (page 53); Neil takes a big step to remove a big rock before it gets stuck in the harvester (pages 54 & 55); a freshly harvested Crane Brothers field in morning fog (pages 56 & 57).*

*Thanks to that frost, every year there's a new crop of rocks. I've picked rocks since I was big enough to walk and I'll probably pick rocks till I can't walk anymore.*

—Neil Crane
Crane Brothers Farm

---

NEIL CLEARS A ROCK FROM THE PATH OF THE HARVESTER

# Horsepower Farm

*We know that in 1880, they raised some dry beans the way we do and they had some sheep and they had a number of cattle and the surprising thing is that they had a team of horses. They were doing a lot of the same things we've done on this farm for the past 40 years. So a lot of the same things have been going on here for 200 years.*

— Paul Birdsall
Horsepower Farm

A GUEST ENTERS PAUL BIRDSALL'S home through a large mudroom that is also used to weigh and pack vegetables—a first indication that this is indeed a working farmhouse. You next come to the kitchen—not the kind of kitchen pictured in country living magazines, but one that shows the wear of preparing thousands of meals. The room extends into a large living area. The floors are wide pine boards flecked here and there with mud; the ceilings are low and look their age. There's an old wooden table full of papers and farm journals, and floor-to-ceiling shelves full of books of all sorts. There's a rocker on the far side of the hearth, where Paul usually sits, and a comfortable chair across from it. At the far end of the room rests his late wife Molly's treasured piano.

Tea is offered. And Paul's wide smile invites conversation.

Paul loves people as much as farming. He's farmed here for over 35 years, raising a broad variety of vegetables, as well as some grains and livestock. But in some ways his primary crop has been people, people who are passionate about food and farming. He's been a mentor to countless farm apprentices who lived on the farm as they worked here, sharing labor, meals, values, and friendship. Because it has now happened to me so many times, I am no longer surprised to encounter farmers and foodies—in Maine and beyond—who Paul Birdsall has taught and touched.

Paul also loves workhorses. The work that is done on most farms with tractors is done mostly by horses here. Just beyond the dooryard lies a large collection of horse-drawn equipment, both antiques and relatively new items, mostly Amish built—altogether a fascinating array of plows and planters, cultivators and harvesters. Horse and man farm together here, putting these ingenious tools to productive use.

Horsepower Farm consists of over 300 acres of fields and forests located along a ribbon of good soils in the town of Penobscot, on the beautiful Blue Hill peninsula.

The Maine coast conjures up images of lighthouses and lobster, but rarely farms. Yet farming was once common in coastal regions, in part because of good access to markets. Local farms could often service the Boston market, because for much of Maine's history—until well into the early twentieth century—so many ships plied the coast between Boston and points downeast. Local demand was often also strong, because of summer visitors

---

*The entrance to Horsepower Farm in Penobscot, Maine (page 58); apprentices driving the horses out to field; Paul with one of the horses; the farmstead beyond a field of peas (page 59, left to right); Paul hanging out with the apprentices, picking rocks, and collecting eggs (page 60, clockwise); an apprentice gathers hay for the horses (page 61).*

who began coming to the Maine coast in numbers in the late 1800s. In communities like Blue Hill, the demand for local farm products has now returned, and most of the pockets of good soils that remain undeveloped are as viable for farming today as they were a century ago.

The biggest challenge to farming in popular coastal regions is affordable farmland. There are plenty of people wanting to farm, but high land prices make it difficult, if not impossible, for would-be farmers to acquire good land. The best solution is to permanently preserve more farmland. A well-crafted agricultural easement not only prevents a farm from being developed, but also means that when the current owner sells (whether immediately or long into the future), another farmer will have a chance to buy the property at its "farmland" value.

Paul Birdsall has been a force behind preserving over 1,600 acres of farmland in this region. Blue Hill Heritage Trust began placing easements on farm properties long before other local land trusts were thinking about farms, and did so—in no small measure—because of the vision and persistence of one of its board members, Paul. He has not only donated an easement

on Horsepower Farm, but facilitated many other deals on the peninsula. In some instances, he has bought farmland, preserved it, and then resold it to new farmers. (In this way, he helped create the model for one of Maine Farmland Trust's principal programs, called "Buy/Protect/Sell.")

Horsepower Farm is run today by Paul along with his son Andy and daughter-in-law Donna, and their grown son Drew. Paul is fast to point out that Andy and Donna deserve most of the credit for the farm's current success, as they grow and sell all the vegetables, but Paul's ongoing role is not to be underestimated. His current focus is on passing along his horse skills to his grandson. And as Drew has now started his own family, it's quite possible that four generations will be working together on the property before Paul stops farming.

Legacy is the word that comes to mind when I think of Paul. He has created with his family a successful farm that is not only

a model for farming today, but also keeps alive know-how from another time, skills that I'm convinced we will need again in the future. He is also personally and directly responsible for getting so many young people into farming, and for saving so much good land.

Paul tries to end each summer workday with a swim in his farm pond, joined by whoever else is game. It's a time to cool down and unwind. And it's another time for him to connect with people he cares about, to talk and to listen. As with the animals he tends, the crops he grows, and the land he stewards, Paul is constantly giving back.

*Horsepower storms by (pages 62 & 63); Paul tilling with horsepower (page 64); an apprentice at work on a new field (above); after a day's work on the farm, Paul takes a late autumn swim in the farm pond (pages 66 & 67).*

*We've lost hundreds of thousands of acres of farmland to development, but there's still a lot left and I think we could be the breadbasket of the Northeast. Somebody who wants to move to Maine and farm organically, sustainably, is going to find Maine quite hospitable.*

— Paul Birdsall
Horsepower Farm

PAUL TAKES A LATE AUTUMN SWIM IN THE FARM POND

# Quills End Farm

*Every year our children get to see real life—birth, life, and death. These are things that we've been trying to shield our society from for 50 years. Farm kids get joy and heartbreak and reality wrapped into every season.*

— Philip Retberg
Quills End Farm

PHILIP AND HEATHER RETBERG are like many young farmers who come to Maine Farmland Trust hoping to own a farm. The couple had prior farming experience, having both homesteaded and managed a farm elsewhere, so they knew the skill and effort that farm work demanded. But they also knew that this is what they wanted to do, how they wanted to live their lives, and raise their family.

Like many people who start farms, the Retbergs combine practicality with idealism. Their lives are grounded in the everyday work that is farming, but through their toil, they clearly sense that they are part of something larger than themselves. To me, this new breed of farmer is clearly making a difference—not only in their own communities but also in the world. I view these farmers as twenty-first-century pioneers, carving a life out of a different kind of wilderness while blazing a trail for others to follow.

Quills End Farm is a hub of activity. The Retbergs maintain a beef herd of 20 to 25 head and finish 10 steers a year; they have a growing herd of sheep, and finish about 10 lambs each spring. They also raise 10 hogs, 1,000 meat birds, and another 120 layers, plus they keep two dairy cows. They sell meat and eggs and milk, all direct from their farm. They also make cheese, which they barter, and sell firewood they cut. Their large garden fills many of the family's needs, though they also rely on neighboring farmers, especially in spring when they are so busy with lambing and calving. Thinking ahead, they recently planted fruit trees and raspberries.

The 105-acre property contained only 17 acres of open fields when the Retbergs bought it, although 70 acres were open in the 1940s. Philip has been busy reclaiming the land, creating new fields and pasture where he can. It's hard work.

"The outlay of time and money is immense on land that hasn't been actively managed for thirty years," explains Philip. "It's not

*Benjamin and Alexander help Philip haul logs out of a forested section of the property in preparation to transition the area into grazing lands (page 68); Heather sits with Carolyn after the whole family pitched in to harvest grapes (above).*

just a matter of removing trees and stumps, but of restoring soils that have become acidic and lost fertility."

Philip also works off the farm, as a builder. But as the farm has grown, Philip has put in less time at his other job. This past year—for the first time—he stepped away from construction work and devoted six months full time to the farm. The hope is that he can continue to do that in future years. If so, it will be a huge step forward in the life he and Heather want for their family. "We hope we're raising another generation of farmers," says Philip.

Heather home schools their three children, who not only help with chores, but also take on specific roles. Carolyn, age 4, washes eggs. Benjamin, age 7, splits firewood. Alexander, age 11, butchers chickens—a role he began at age 8. Alexander also raises ducks. It's his own enterprise, and one he takes full responsibility for.

As committed to farming as the Retbergs are, the life they are creating at Quills End Farm is only possible because the land they bought had been preserved. Otherwise, they could not afford to buy 105 acres on the desirable Blue Hill peninsula. They are indebted to another local farmer, Paul Birdsall, who bought this land when it came up for sale, preserved it through the local land trust, and then sold it to Philip and Heather at its new, lower "farmland" value.

A lot of misconceptions exist about what happens when a farm is preserved through an easement. A well-constructed agricultural easement is designed with great flexibility, because the goal is to keep the land viable for agriculture long into the future, and no one can predict that future. Easements prevent subdivision and removal of topsoil, but generally allow fencing, farm buildings, and land clearing that might be needed to keep a farm vibrant.

For these reasons, most farmers who understand easements are comfortable owning preserved land. And increasingly, farmers like the Retbergs are seeking to buy preserved farmland, because it comes at a lower price. Saving money on land is often necessary to get a new farmer started. But even where it's not a necessity, keeping land costs down frees up funds for investing in the farm's operation; and with so many Maine farms having seen at least some past neglect, there is often plenty of need to invest.

Smart, talented people like Philip and Heather Retberg could always make more money doing something else, but to even think that misses the point. "We're in it for the life, not the living," explains Philip. "And we wouldn't trade it for the world."

The Retberg's life is interwoven with the lives of other farmers in the region. "We couldn't make it without each other and the infrastructure that comes from a certain density of farmers in one area," explains Heather. "Before we moved here, Paul Birdsall told us how he was not just trying to preserve farmland, but to get enough next generation farmers here so that we can support each other."

And that is exactly what is happening, and not only on the Blue Hill peninsula. In an increasing number of places across the state, the community of farmers is growing. That is often what's necessary to serve growing markets. But it also has a personal side.

---

*Alexander cleans and prepares his pasture-raised eggs for sale at his roadside farm stand; Carolyn takes a nap amid the freshly split firewood; Philip and Alexander walk home after harvesting grapes for jelly (page 70, clockwise); Alexander goofs around in the hay feeder at dusk (pages 72 & 73).*

Heather has many stories. One took place in the middle of a January storm, with Philip out of action due to a recent surgery. Faced with delivering a difficult calf alone, Heather called farmer friends to help her. The friends came quickly and the calf was delivered safely while other friends came and fed the Retberg family that night.

Says Heather: "We believed when we began—and still do—in a life lived close to nature, woven into the fabric of community, supporting others as the land supports us."

*Philip sits with his Galloway steers after feeding them an evening treat of beet pulp (page 74); Carolyn helps feed the chickens; Alexander and Heather harvest the garden in late autumn; Benjamin helps Philip herd the sheep to move them to another section of grazing field; Philip gets comfortable with the idea of having goats on the farm (above, clockwise); Philip and Alexander harvest grapes together (pages 76 & 77); Philip and Heather spend sweet time with their animals (pages 78 & 79); Alexander totes Benjamin out to the field for some sledding (pages 80 & 81).*

*The farm unto itself is an ecosystem. Our crop is grass. Our harvesters are chickens and cattle and pigs and lambs and all the microbes and earthworms and everything that live off what we do as we rotationally graze our animals. The entire ecosystem benefits from it; it increases the fertility of the soil, it increases its ability to capture sunlight and do that incredible photosynthesis thing that feeds all life. So by grazing animals, we sell photosynthesis. Our job is to steward the land with the resources we are given: sunlight, water, earth, and photosynthesis.*

— Philip Retberg
Quills End Farm

PHILIP AND ALEXANDER HARVESTING GRAPES

*I enjoy what my animals produce, but I don't view my animals as production units. We let our animals express their animalness. Our job is to facilitate animals being animals as they were intended to be.*
*It takes more time and resources, and it takes caring.*

— Philip Retberg
Quills End Farm

*It seems like we spend all of spring and summer and fall getting ready for the winter.*

—Alexander Retberg (age 11)
Quills End Farm

---

ALEXANDER TOTES BENJAMIN OUT TO SLED

*If you have a sense of place, if you have a sense of community, and perhaps a sense of history, you'll care for the land.*

— Steve Miller
Miller Farm

FARMS IN MAINE come in all flavors, so it's risky to generalize. Aroostook County is known for large potato farms, but you can find a diverse collection of farms there, too—including some surprises.

For 35 years, Steve and Barbara Miller have tenderly cared for 85 acres of woods and fields in the northern Aroostook town of Westmanland. They know and love their land as few property owners ever do. For all those years, the land has been their life, providing much of their food, fuel, day's work, and evening's contemplation. They have shaped the land, but mostly the land has shaped them. It has taught them about nature, community, and history. The Millers have been both stewards and students, both overseers and observers.

Steve and Barbara grow most of what they eat, bartering for some things they don't raise. Beyond a homestead garden, they harvest a wide variety of berries, keep bees, and raise goats. They sell some products at the local farmers market. They also grow nursery stock for FEDCO, a Maine-based mail order company. These activities have not provided much income, but the Millers live off it.

Much of this land is wooded. Steve revels in the four-foot-wide stumps that remain scattered about the property, a sign of the great forest that once stood here. And for him, a sign of what this land can be again. He takes issue with a strictly utilitarian view of woodlands, believing that a well-managed forest must serve a deeper biological purpose than simply a sustainable harvest.

He and Barbara have worked hard to help the forest they steward return to a natural equilibrium. They had the benefit of woods that hadn't been cut hard since 1910, and that boasted a few trees over 200 years old. They now manage a biologically diverse forest that produces wood without cutting the older trees or jeopardizing the forest's return to a more natural state.

*Barbara and Steve take a Sunday walk in their woodlot behind the farm (page 82); The goats follow Barbara from the barn after feeding (above); Steve takes a rest in the barn door long enough to attract a friend to come visit (page 84); Barbara makes organic goat's milk yogurt in the kitchen; Steve tends to his organic honeybees; Steve harvests the blueberries that the Millers sell fresh and use to flavor Steve's famous honeys (page 85, clockwise).*

"This piece of woods is our statement that these things are important," says Steve.

Years ago the Millers built a simple house. They heat with wood they cut. The only electricity is solar. Water comes from an outdoor hand pump that is fifty feet from their house.

Steve and Barbara clearly love this property. They have a profound appreciation of how important it is for them to do all they can for this land that is in their care. Many of us espouse such principles, but the Millers truly live them.

They say that the decision to donate an easement on this land was easy, because they felt so strongly that it must be preserved. But I can't help but feel it must have been difficult to entrust anyone else with the responsibility to care for this special treasure, their farm, their life's work. Maine Farmland Trust is humbled by the trust Steve and Barbara have placed in us.

The Millers recently built a new house on the property, another simple dwelling, into which they have moved. A family of four is now living in the "old house," working the land as well. Steve and Barbara are hopeful that this new family will stay, and that over time will learn to love this place as they do.

No longer young, the Millers know that they will not be able to farm forever. "The easement gives us the freedom to leave," says Steve. "Without it, we'd feel like we'd have to stay beyond when perhaps we should."

Now if the Millers need to sell, they know that Maine Farmland Trust will stand guard over their legacy, ensuring that the new owners—whether it's the family living there now or someone else—will be held to high standards.

But for Steve and Barbara, the importance of preserving farmland extends far beyond their own property. They see the big picture. They know that what they are doing has value, but that it has much more value as part of a broader movement. They understand that so much more is needed, all across the state.

Steve Miller makes the case for Maine Farmland Trust's work as well as anyone:

"If you don't have the land base, you don't have the possibility of farms, the possibility of agriculture. Human communities depend on people producing food, and a level of stewardship to ensure the land is not degraded. There is nothing more important to leave for the people who follow than preserved farmland."

*Barbara and Steve harvesting blueberries together; Steve sharpening his sickle to mow fields and gardens (page 86, top to bottom); Steve towing his chainsaw to harvest firewood (above); Barbara and Steve bringing the harvest gear in after a long summer day in the berry rows (pages 88 & 89).*

# Coda

## John Piotti

I OFTEN ASK YOUNG FARMERS how they came to this life. Perhaps they grew up on a farm. Or perhaps a friend urged them to try a farm apprenticeship and something stuck. Or maybe they just love farm animals. Or they enjoy good food. Their answers vary. But if I probe, I invariably learn that—regardless of circumstances—they all share a belief that, as farmers, they are contributing in some meaningful way to the future. And indeed they are.

I am not a farmer. (Susan and I can only claim a home garden, a few chickens, and a transient horse or two.) But for much of my career, farming has been my focus and my passion. I came to this work through two unrelated experiences—my youth living on an island and my adult friendship with a dairy farmer.

My father was killed when I was young, and soon afterward my mother moved us to Nantucket Island, where the family had come as visitors. (As a nurse, she could find a job there.) My years on the island healed me and shaped me. My mother remarried a seventh generation islander who taught me to hunt and fish, and who tended a large garden from which my mother put up vegetables for winter. Nantucket's natural beauty and an engaging teacher inspired me to become a student of ecology, and I took to exploring the island's woods, moorland, and salt marshes. Meanwhile, I became part of a close-knit rural community.

Nantucket then was different than today. No place stays the same, but Nantucket went through some profound changes in the years after I graduated from high school. The 1980s sparked both a building boom and skyrocketing property values, driven in part by technological and workplace changes that enabled people with summer connections to move there. Almost all of my high school friends were from old island families, but many could not afford to return to Nantucket after time at college or in military service. Nor could I go home. By then my stepfather had died and my mother had moved off island, so I didn't have a foothold. But the primary reason—which hit me squarely during a reflective summer between college and graduate school—was that there were no opportunities for me there.

Why was it that rural communities seemed destined to either wither away or become overbuilt and unaffordable like Nantucket (or Manchester, Vermont, where Susan was raised)? Why couldn't rural Maine—for example—go down a different path, one where economic vibrancy doesn't equate with excessive new development and doesn't push local people out? Why couldn't Maine sustain itself?

Susan and I settled in Unity in 1988. Over time, we made an old farmhouse livable, and slower still, became part of the community. I started a consulting business built around the notion of sustainable development, in which I helped the kinds of small businesses that I thought could grow in Maine without spoiling the place. I never thought of working with farmers.

A dairy farmer named Dick Perkins changed that. I found myself co-chairing Unity's Comprehensive Plan Committee with Dick. Once we began to work together, and he had sized me up, he began to challenge me. "You say you want to help support rural Maine, but you know nothing about farming!"

Dick spurred me to learn about farming, and one thing led to another. I began to realize how little I knew. I had received one of the best educations money could buy; I had committed myself to rural Maine; but my thoughts about farming were shallow, stereotypical, and often wrong.

I began to see farming's promise. I began to see that unlike most other businesses, farming could grow in ways that actually enhanced the land. More importantly, I became convinced that Maine could only hope to sustain itself with vibrant farms. Clearly, farms were our future!

I had found my work.

A dozen years ago, Dick Perkins moved his family north to Charleston, where he took over his uncle's farm. His operation grew, most recently as his son and daughter completed college and returned home to join the business. Like many dairy farmers, the Perkins rely on large tracts of cropland they don't own. A year ago, Dick called me when they were about to lose some choice land. Maine Farmland Trust bought a vulnerable farm in the area, preserved it, and now leases it to the Perkins, who plan to buy it from us soon. The new cropland is invaluable to them. Dick's daughter and son-in-law now live in the property's farmhouse, where they watch over the heifers and dry cows in the barn. On a recent visit, Dick enthusiastically outlined his plans to fix up the barn and improve the fields.

There is always more work to do.

# Field Notes

## Bridget Besaw

I SEEK OUT PHOTOGRAPHY PROJECTS that will put me in nature alongside people who have a deep understanding of nature's processes. Fishermen, wilderness guides, ecologists, and farmers. Being with these people reminds me of my own earthy instincts and skills, and offers new lessons in how to live more simply and happily.

In the spring of 2007, Maine Farmland Trust (MFT), under John Piotti's leadership, decided to convey the importance of protecting farmland by commissioning a series of artful photographs. After discussions about the scope of the project, I am grateful that John and his board set me free, creatively speaking, on a collection of the farms they were working with. They literally set me out to pasture!

Maine Farmland Trust's support of art as a means of promoting their work is a bold and progressive approach to say the least, and John took a leap of faith in me. Out of MFT's trust and boldness came a set of large prints that have toured galleries, cafes, colleges, food fairs, and the Maine State House to help raise awareness about MFT's efforts.

In 2009 when asked to support a book project, the MFT board again showed their progressive approach to conservation by choosing visual art and storytelling to help accomplish their goals. MFT has a gallery space below their offices in Belfast, and their tagline is "Celebrating art in agriculture." It seems the partnership between artists and conservation organizations is proving to be a powerful tool to reach all kinds of people with a message about environmental protection.

It was a privilege to get to know the people in the pages of this book. They taught me a great deal about growing and raising healthy food for the people of Maine, and by example, they shared with me what I've come to think of as the secret of good living: having a thoughtful, respectful relationship with the land that sustains us. Through them I have learned that small-scale, local farmers are on the forefront of our struggle to circle back to the connection between the health of the earth and our physical and emotional well-being.

While we can't all farm the land and create food for our families or communities, we can learn a thing or two from those who do. When the primary tools of your trade are sun, soil, and water, a graceful comfort and ease with nature's cycles sets in—something many of us can barely remember from childhood. Countless peaceful sunrises and sunsets await our discovery when we become more in tune with the time of day they happen, and make an effort to experience them in the outdoors.

When we support a farm family by buying their products or by helping to preserve the land they need to continue farming, we participate in a circle of ecological, financial, and cultural sustainability that connects us to the land by simply asking us to be more mindful about where our food comes from.

I hope these pictures and this book will help nurture a growing collective curiosity about food, farmland, and farm culture.

# About Maine Farmland Trust

MAINE FARMLAND TRUST (MFT) is a statewide nonprofit organization that protects Maine's precious farmland and keeps farms working. MFT exists not only to save farmland, but also to help make farming more vital and viable. Membership is open to everyone.

Since our founding in 1999, MFT has assisted over 200 farmers and farmland owners and helped protect over 22,000 acres of Maine farmland. MFT works closely with dozens of local and regional land trusts, many of which have an interest in farming and farmland, but do not have the expertise.

MFT's focus on working farms is unique and critically important to the future of Maine.

MFT's goal is to preserve 100,000 acres of farmland by 2014. This goal is ambitious but necessary, given that so many acres of Maine's best farmland will be in transition in the next few years. We believe that this scale of activity is needed if we are to make a meaningful impact.

MFT is aggressively pursuing this goal through four programs:

**AGRICULTURAL EASEMENTS:** MFT permanently preserves farmland through both donated and purchased easements. Agricultural easements prevent subdivision and removal of prime soils, but allow for a great deal of flexibility, as long as the activities support farming.

FARMLINK: This program connects farmers seeking land with retiring farmers and other farmland owners who wish to see their land remain in agriculture. Many of the participants are young farmers who have gained skills through apprenticeships with other farmers, and who are now seeking land of their own.

BUY/PROTECT/SELL (BPS): Through this program, MFT purchases vulnerable farmland, permanently preserves it through an easement, and then sells it to a farmer at a more affordable "farmland value." Sometimes a young farmer participating in FarmLink buys the land. Other deals are designed to support existing farmers who are looking to either expand their holdings or secure land they currently lease.

FARM VIABILITY: Another way to protect farmland is to help farmers make a living on the land, so that they remain in business. MFT draws on a network of agricultural experts and resources to help existing farmers initiate new operations, reach new markets, or take other steps to enhance future success.

MFT cannot fulfill its promise without a growing body of members who care deeply about the future of farming in Maine. For more information, please visit www.mainefarmlandtrust.org.

www.bridgetbesaw.com
www.greenmediateam.org



Quote interviews and editing by Bridget Besaw, Portland, Maine
Edited by Elizabeth IlgenFritz, South Montville, Maine
Designed and produced by Harrah Lord, Yellow House Studio, Rockport, Maine
Printed in China through Four Colour Print Group, Louisville, Kentucky.

Library of Congress Control Number: 2010908047
ISBN 978-0-9797624-1-3
First Edition

Everbest is an FSC certified printing plant.
This book has been printed on FSC text paper and cover stock.

**CPSIA Information**
Plant Location: Printed by Everbest Printing Co. Ltd., Nansha, China
Production Date: June 8, 2010
Job/Batch #: EPC-RN-95195.2 R5

With support from Leica Camera Inc.